Solo
Début
Series

Easy *Recorder* Sol
Playalong Showtu

CW00392077

Wise Publications
part of The Music Sales Group
London/New York/Paris/Sydney/Copenhagen/Berlin/Madrid/Tokyo

Published by
Wise Publications
14-15 Berners Street, London W1T 3LJ, UK.

Exclusive Distributors:
Music Sales Limited
Distribution Centre, Newmarket Road, Bury St Edmunds, Suffolk IP33 3YB, UK.
Music Sales Pty Limited
120 Rothschild Avenue, Rosebery, NSW 2018, Australia.

Order No. AM986084
ISBN 1-84609-613-8
This book © Copyright 2006 Wise Publications,
a division of Music Sales Limited.

Arranging and engraving supplied by Camden Music.
Compiled by Heather Slater.
Cover design by Chloe Alexander.
Printed in the EU.

CD recorded, mixed and mastered by John Rose and Jonas Persson.
Instrumental solos by Andy Findon.
New backing tracks arranged by Paul Honey.
Melody line arrangements by Christopher Hussey.

Your Guarantee of Quality
As publishers, we strive to produce every book to the highest commercial standards.
The music has been freshly engraved and the book has been carefully designed to minimise
awkward page turns and to make playing from it a real pleasure.
Particular care has been given to specifying acid-free, neutral-sized paper made from pulps
which have not been elemental chlorine bleached. This pulp is from farmed sustainable forests
and was produced with special regard for the environment.
Throughout, the printing and binding have been planned to ensure a sturdy, attractive
publication which should give years of enjoyment.
If your copy fails to meet our high standards, please inform us and we will gladly replace it.

www.musicsales.com

FREE bonus material downloadable to your computer.
Visit: www.hybridpublications.com
Registration is free and easy.
Your registration code is: TF129

Fingering Chart 4

Performance Tips 6

All I Ask Of You *from* **The Phantom Of The Opera** 14

Cabaret *from* **Cabaret** 11

Can't Help Lovin' Dat Man *from* **Showboat** 16

Don't Cry For Me Argentina *from* **Evita** 18

I Dreamed A Dream *from* **Les Misérables** 22

Hopelessly Devoted To You *from* **Grease** 20

Mamma Mia *from* **Mamma Mia!** 24

Some Enchanted Evening *from* **South Pacific** 26

Take That Look Off Your Face *from* **Tell Me On A Sunday** 28

Tell Me It's Not True *from* **Blood Brothers** 30

Recorder Fingering Chart

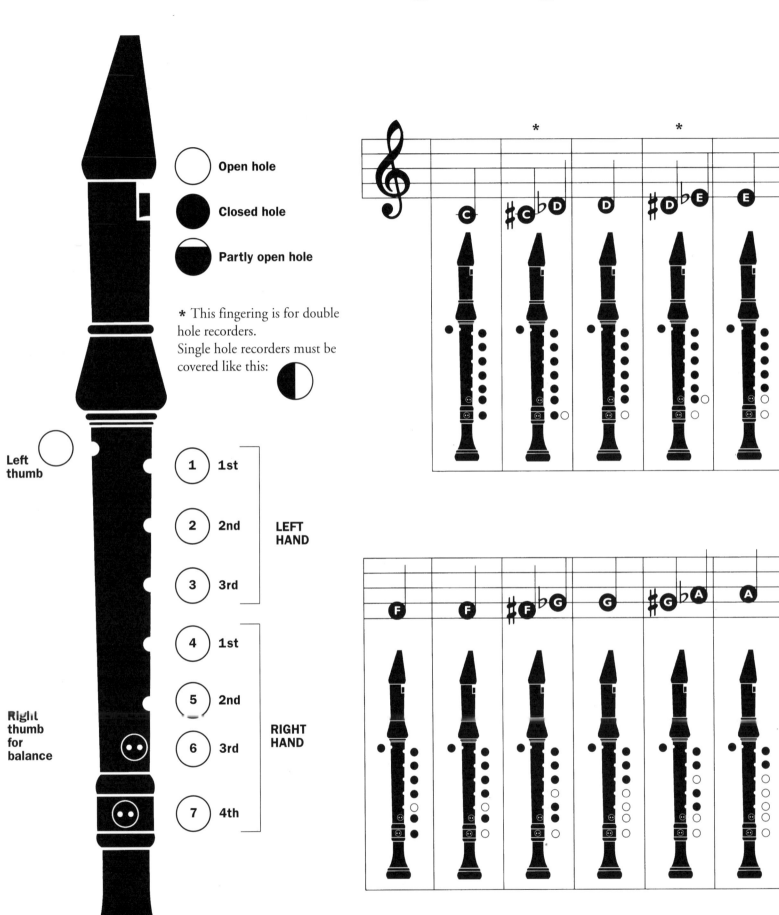

Open hole

Closed hole

Partly open hole

* This fingering is for double hole recorders.
Single hole recorders must be covered like this:

Left thumb

1	1st
2	2nd	LEFT HAND
3	3rd

4	1st
5	2nd
6	3rd	RIGHT HAND
7	4th

Right thumb for balance

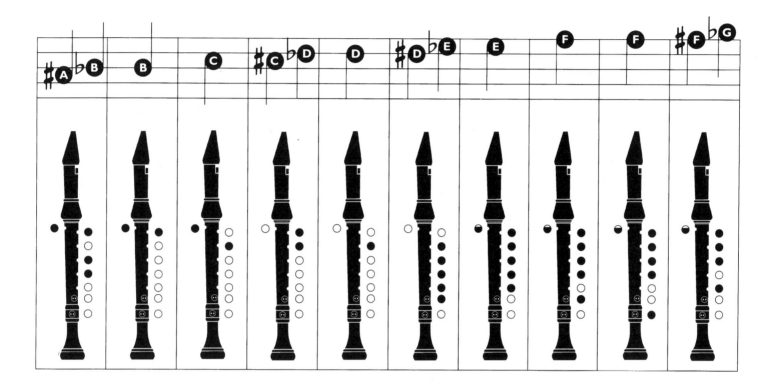
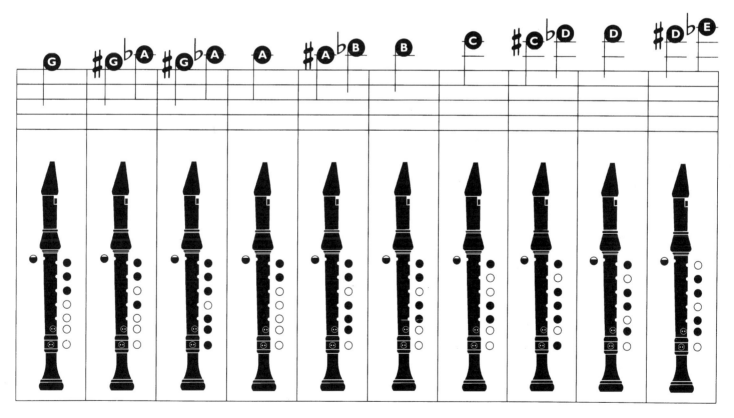

PERFORMANCE TIPS

Welcome to this exciting collection of playalong tunes from some of your favourite musicals!

Before you begin to play, make sure your instrument is in tune (there are tuning notes on Track 1 of the CD) and listen to the demonstration performances on Tracks 2–11 while following along with the music.

Throughout the book, you'll notice some tiny notes written into the music—these are called **cues**, and they are not to be played. They show you what is happening on the backing track (i.e. what the other instruments are playing) so that you will know when to come in.

Below are some practice tips and suggestions to help you improve your performance.

CABARET (from 'Cabaret')

- Listen to the demonstration performance all the way through before trying to play along with the backing track—some of the tempo changes may come as a surprise!

- An important feature of this song is **syncopation**. A syncopated rhythm occurs when beats of the bar which are normally unaccented are given an accent. The first example of syncopated rhythm occurs in bars 7 and 8:

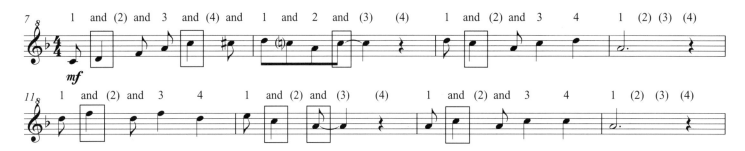

- The syncopation in bar 7 occurs on the 'and' of the 1st beat and the 'and' of the 3rd beat. In bar 8 there is a syncopated accent on the 'and' of the 2nd beat. Practise this passage as it is written above (i.e. without any articulation) until you are confident with the rhythm.

- Most of the quavers in this song have **articulation marks**—either **staccato** dots (indicating that the notes should be tongued and played shorter than written) or **tenuto** lines (indicating that the notes should be tongued and given their full value). Play this passage again as it is written in your music (bars 7-14), and notice how the articulation gives character to the melody.

ALL I ASK OF YOU (from 'The Phantom Of The Opera')

- There are a number of different quaver and semiquaver rhythms to master in this song, including: Practise the passage in bars 3–6 several times in order to master some of these combinations.

- There are also some tricky time signature changes, so practise the following passage (bars 15–21), counting very carefully as you play, to help you with the $\frac{2}{4}$ and $\frac{3}{4}$ bars:

CAN'T HELP LOVIN' DAT MAN (from 'Showboat')

- This much-loved ballad is played with a swing feel—once you have mastered this, you will find playing in this jazz style to be quite natural and fun!

  At the top of your music you'll see the following marking: ♩♩ = ♩♩♩

  This means that all 'straight' quavers (♩♩) are to be 'swung' as follows:

- Practise the passage below (bars 5–11)—the slurs have been removed, so you will need to tongue each note:

- Now play the same passage with the slurs in place, exactly as they appear in your music (see below). Place a slight accent on the first quaver of each slurred pair, which always occurs on the 'offbeat'—this is the standard way of phrasing 'swung' quavers in jazz music:

- In the very last bar (bar 81) there is a 'fermata', or 'pause', mark (𝄐). This indicates that the note should be held for a few beats longer than written.

DON'T CRY FOR ME ARGENTINA (from 'Evita')

- A rhythmic feature of this well-known song is the crotchet triplet figure that first appears in bar 10. The passage below (bars 12–19) includes several crotchet triplets. Have a look at the first one in bar 14—notice that there is a bracket with a '3' in the middle, just above the first three crotchets of the bar. This means that the three crotchets should be played in the time of two, like this:

Practise this passage several times to master the crotchet triplet rhythm, counting carefully as you do so:

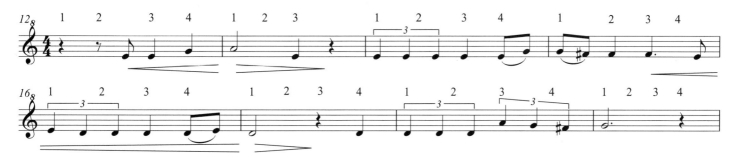

- Watch out for the F♯ accidentals in bars 15 and 18. There is a bracketed natural sign before the F in bar 20—this is called a **cautionary accidental**, and it is there to remind you that the F should be natural again, as in the key signature.

HOPELESSLY DEVOTED TO YOU (from 'Grease')

- Practise the passage below (bars 24–34), counting carefully as you do so. You will encounter a number of two-note slurs and a long one over three notes in bars 27–28—these should be played all in one breath and without tonguing:

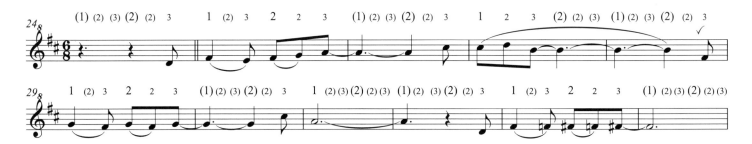

- Watch out for the accidentals (for example, in bars 17 and 19) and the abrupt key changes between D major and B♭ major.
- Practise the passage below (bars 43–50) to make sure you know which notes are flat and which are natural in B♭ major:

I DREAMED A DREAM (from 'Les Misérables')

- Practise the opening phrase (bars 5–8), paying particular attention to the dotted quaver-semiquaver rhythms, and also to the slurring of the quavers in bars 5, 7 and 8:

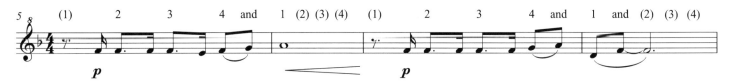

- In bar 41 the song changes key from F major to G major—remember that the Bs are no longer flat and all Fs are now sharp. Practise the passage below (bars 41–48) to get used to playing the tune in G major, and watch out for the quaver triplets (bars 41, 43, 45 and 47):

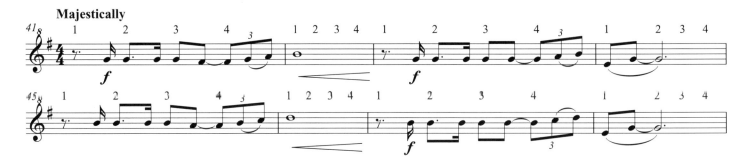

- Practise the passage below (bars 49–54) and notice that your first phrase, beginning in bar 50, starts later than usual, after the tune has begun on the backing track—in bars 50 and 52 you are playing an 'answering phrase' to the main tune, catching up with the tune again in bar 53:

- The last note of bar 56 and the note in bar 57 are played without any accompaniment, so be confident and count carefully to make sure you place them correctly.

MAMMA MIA (from 'Mamma Mia!')

- Practise the opening phrase (bars 9–11) to make sure you know where the slurs and syncopated beats occur, and to work on your tonguing:

- The passage below (bars 24–32) contains several articulation marks that give the tune an energetic and bouncy character. There are **staccato** dots (indicating that the notes should be played shorter than written) and **accents** (indicating that you should tongue harder to make these notes stand out). There are also some notes which have a staccato dot *and* an accent—these should be tongued harder and played shorter than written:

- The passage below (bars 37–42) contains a number of syncopated beats, where notes that would normally be unaccented are given an accent—for example, in bar 37 (the note which falls on the 'and' of the 4th beat) and in bar 38 (the notes which fall on the 'and' of the 2nd and 3rd beats). Practise this phrase and count carefully in your head to help you place the notes:

- The tiny notes in the repeated phrase at the end are there to show you what is happening on the backing track, but you can try to play along with this riff if you're daring! If you do, you should gradually get quieter as the music fades away.

SOME ENCHANTED EVENING (from 'South Pacific')

- Watch out for the accidentals in the opening passage—there are F♯s in bars 5, 7 and 9.

- The passage below (bars 12–20) contains several crotchet triplets (for example, in bar 12)—these three crotchets should be played in the time of two crotchet beats (see the Performance Tips for 'Don't Cry For Me Argentina'):

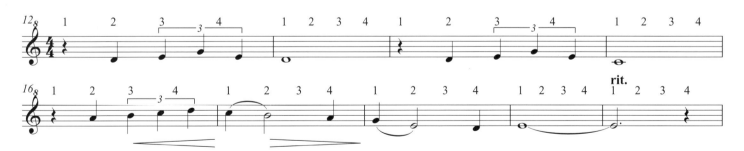

- Be sure to take a big breath where there is a tick (✓) at the end of bar 47 so that you have enough breath to get to the end.

TAKE THAT LOOK OFF YOUR FACE (from 'Tell Me On A Sunday')

- This song has four crotchet beats per bar, but there are several $\frac{2}{4}$ bars throughout. Make sure you know where they are and count carefully in your head as you approach them. Practise the opening phrase below (bars 3–7) to help you master this, and also to work on the syncopated rhythms which feature prominently in this tune:

- The chorus, which first appears on the upbeat into bar 21, also contains syncopated rhythms and $\frac{2}{4}$ bars. Practise the opening of the chorus (bars 21–30) below, to familiarise yourself with this part of the tune:

- When the chorus returns in bar 36, you begin to play later than you would normally—the melody is played on the backing track and you begin by playing two 'answering phrases', then catching up with the melody again at bar 39:

- Take a very large breath during the minim rest at the beginning of bar 47, so that you have enough breath to get to the end of the phrase.

TELL ME IT'S NOT TRUE (from 'Blood Brothers')

- As in 'Take That Look Off Your Face', there are a number of $\frac{2}{4}$ bars inserted into this song, which mainly has four crotchet beats per bar. Practising the opening phrase (bars 3–8) several times will help you to master this:

- Practise the passage below (bars 13–17) to work on the dotted quaver-semiquaver rhythms and the fast semiquavers in bar 14. Be mindful of the slurring in this section and the change of time signature to $\frac{2}{4}$:

Cabaret
(from 'Cabaret')

Music by John Kander

cresc.

f

1:13

mp

mf

mp

rit. 1:40 **slowly, rubato** (c. ♩ = 70)

rit. 1:53

mf *p*

rit.

All I Ask Of You
(from 'The Phantom Of The Opera')

Music by Andrew Lloyd Webber

Can't Help Lovin' Dat Man
(from 'Showboat')

Music by Jerome Kern

(clarinet)

(muted trumpets)

Don't Cry For Me Argentina
(from 'Evita')

Music by Andrew Lloyd Webber

19

Hopelessly Devoted To You
(from 'Grease')

Music by John Farrar

I Dreamed A Dream
(from 'Les Misérables')

Music by Claude-Michel Schönberg

Mamma Mia
(from 'Mamma Mia!')

Words & Music by Benny Andersson, Stig Anderson & Björn Ulvaeus

Some Enchanted Evening
(from 'South Pacific')

Music by Richard Rodgers

Take That Look Off Your Face
(from 'Tell Me On A Sunday')

Music by Andrew Lloyd Webber

Tell Me It's Not True
(from 'Blood Brothers')

Music by Willy Russell

Steadily ♩ = 74
(piano)

CD Track Listing

1 Tuning notes

Full instrumental performances…

2 Cabaret *from* **Cabaret**
(Ebb/Kander) Carlin Music Corporation

3 All I Ask Of You *from* **The Phantom Of The Opera**
(Lloyd Webber/Hart) The Really Useful Group

4 Can't Help Lovin' Dat Man *from* **Showboat**
(Hammerstein/Kern) Universal Music Publishing Limited/Chappell Music Limited

5 Don't Cry For Me Argentina *from* **Evita**
(Lloyd Webber/Rice) Evita Music Limitd

6 Hopelessly Devoted To You *from* **Grease**
(Farrar) Famous Music Publishing Limited

7 I Dreamed A Dream *from* **Les Misérables**
(Schönberg/Boublil/Natel/Kretzmer) Alain Boublil Music Overseas Limited

8 Mamma Mia *from* **Mammia Mia!**
(Andersson/Anderson/Ulvaeus) Bocu Music Limited

9 Some Enchanted Evening *from* **South Pacific**
(Hammerstein/Rodgers) EMI Music Publishing Limited

10 Take That Look Off Your Face *from* **Tell Me On A Sunday**
(Lloyd Webber/Black) The Really Useful Group Limited

11 Tell Me It's Not True *from* **Blood Brothers**
(Russell) Timeact Limited

Backing tracks only…

12 Cabaret *from* **Cabaret**
13 All I Ask Of You *from* **The Phantom Of The Opera**
14 Can't Help Lovin' Dat Man *from* **Showboat**
15 Don't Cry For Me Argentina *from* **Evita**
16 Hopelessly Devoted To You *from* **Grease**
17 I Dreamed A Dream *from* **Les Misérables**
18 Mamma Mia *from* **Mamma Mia!**
19 Some Enchanted Evening *from* **South Pacific**
20 Take That Look Off Your Face *from* **Tell Me On A Sunday**
21 Tell Me It's Not True *from* **Blood Brothers**

**To remove your CD from the plastic sleeve, lift the small lip to break the perforations.
Replace the disc after use for convenient storage.**